In memory of my dear, wonderful, and kind dad,
Brendan Grace, who taught me to be a super-
optimist and who showed me how to stick
up for myself from a very early age. My dad
instilled in me the belief that ¨there is no such
thing as the word `can´t¨ and that anything is
possible once we believe in it.

Thank you for believing in me, Dad, and for
always believing in Darlene and her friends.

www.mascotbooks.com

Darlene the Drama Queen Raises the Curtain on Bullying

For more information, please contact:
Mascot Books
620 Herndon Parkway, Suite 320
Herndon, VA 20170
info@mascotbooks.com

Library of Congress Control Number: 2019913217

CPSIA Code: PRT1019A
ISBN-13: 978-1-64543-017-9

Printed in the United States

Raises the Curtain on Bullying

by Mel O' Drama

illustrated by Jason Boucher

I'm Darlene, the Drama Queen,
It's really fun to meet you!
I live right here in Drama Land
With friends who'll love to greet you!

I'm six years old and one big half,
That half is quite exciting.
A whole new number, very soon
My hand will then be writing.

I live inside this castle
With friends who love to play.
They bring new friends to meet me
Almost every single day!

Shakespeare is my dragon,
He's big but really kind.
He loves to bring new friends my way
Who feel they're in a bind.

Comedy is the funny one,
Her smile is sweet and true.
She makes me laugh most every day
And she'll make you laugh too!

Tragedy can be moody,
But we all can be that way.
He helps us understand ourselves
When having a bad day!

Ahhhh, there's my stage of magic,
Where I stand to help each friend
Who comes to me with problems
That they think will never end.

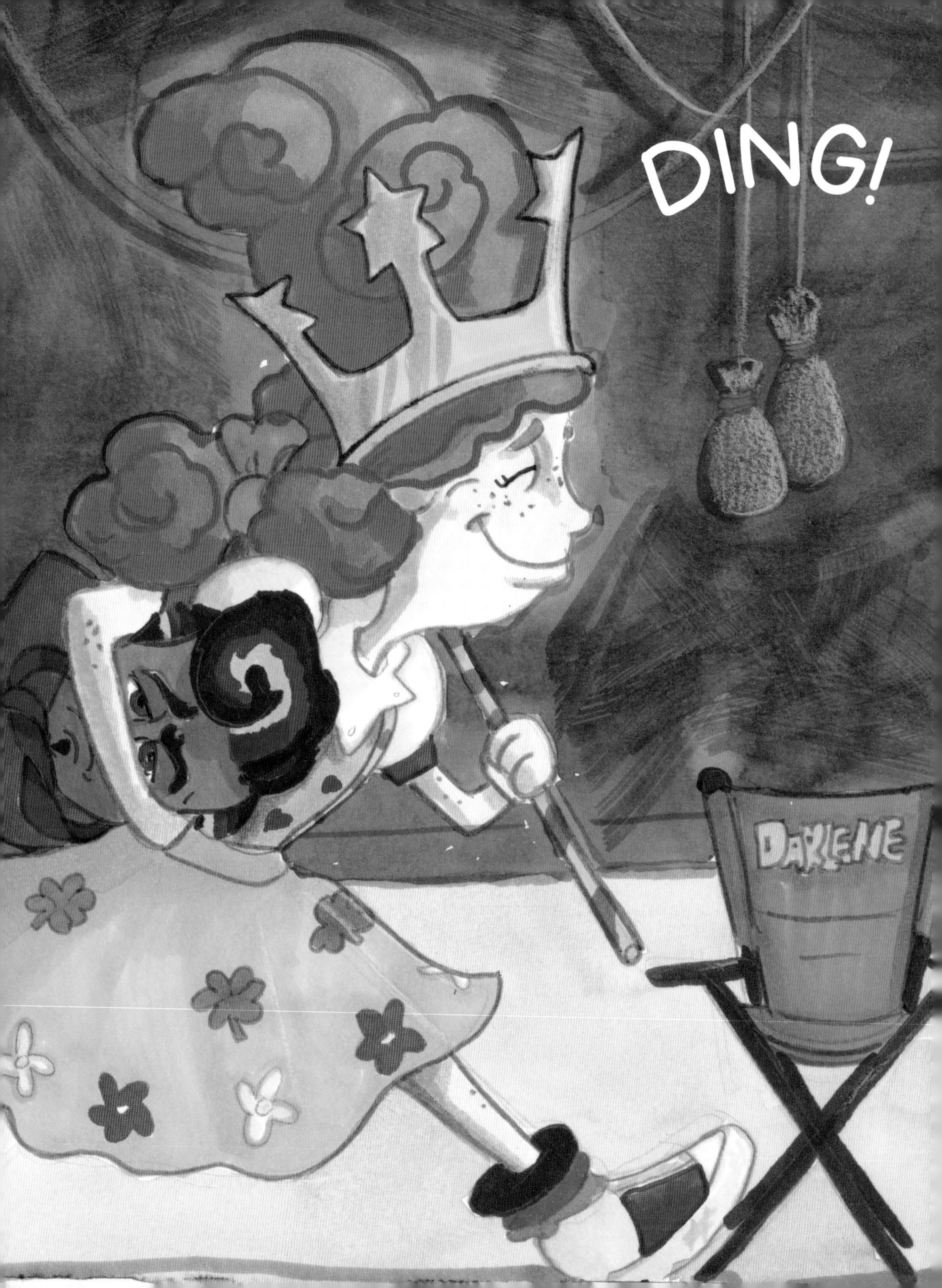
DING!
DARLENE

DONG!

I think I heard the doorbell,
A friend will be here soon.
So let me take my place on stage
And get my skills in tune.

Hey Comedy! Hey Tragedy!
A friend is on the way.
I need your help and some advice
On what to do and say.

"INTRODUCING BOBBY!"

Says Shakespeare with a shout
That makes the boy jump super high
And land down with a pout!

"I'm sorry," explains Shakespeare.
"I know I'm super loud,
But sweet Darlene the Drama Queen
Has taught me to be proud."

Tragedy floats to the boy
With exactly that same pout.
"I don't cope well with noise myself,
In fact, it freaks me out!"

"Oh laugh it off," says Comedy.
"A dragon can't be quiet.
Imagine him with a mouse's voice,
Now that'd be a riot!"

"Let's meet our new friend Bobby,"
Says Darlene over the laughter.
"And when we're through doing what we do
We'll continue laughing after!"

"Hi, my name is Bobby,
I'm feeling very worried.
The kids at school make
fun of me.
I think I'm getting bullied.

They make fun of my freckles
That cover most my face.
They make me feel so sad
And so I've come here to
this place.

I heard from my friend Lucy
That you help her when she's shy.
So maybe you could help me too.
Do you think that you could try?"

"You betcha," says Darlene
As she takes her place on stage.
"Get ready to feel awesome
And to turn a brand new page.

Freckles, from my research
Are actually signs of beauty.
So tell those bullies next time
That they're dealing with a CUTIE!

And something else exciting:
Freckles mean you're smart!
So when the bullies point them out
Don't take it to your heart.

If you believe you're awesome
And you are, look at yourself!
The bullies won't have power.
They'll be left up on the shelf!"

"When cruel words are thrown your way
Just keep a steady mind.
Don't be like the other guys,
Remember YOU are kind!

Throw on your cloak of confidence,
Pretend you're in a play.
Shoulders back and stand up tall
And this is what you say...

`Thanks for the information,
It's too bad you feel that way.´

It will take away their power
A little bit each day.

Then walk toward an adult
Who you feel that you can trust.
Bullies won't have fun with that,
Their plan will be a bust!"

"YOU GO BOY," shouts out Comedy.
"GO GET `EM," Tragedy cries.
"You've got this," shouts out Shakespeare,
"You are HANDSOME, SMART, and WISE!"

"Thank you everybody,
I'm in such a happy state.
And when bullies try to make me cry
I'll show them that I'm GREAT!"

BRAVO! We've helped another friend
Upon our magic stage.

I wonder who will visit next.
Her name? Or his? Their age?

The Cloak of Confidence

Three Things I Really Like About Myself

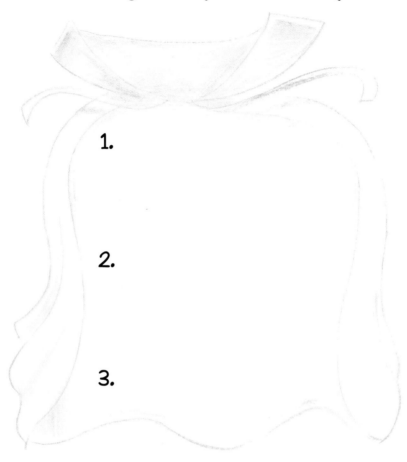

1.

2.

3.

MANTRA

(Say this in the mirror every day)

I am great. I am unique. There is only ONE of me! I like so many things about myself, especially the three things I've listed above. I will be the best ME I can be today. If somebody tries to hurt me with their mean words, I will say, "It's too bad you feel that way" and then I will walk away remembering all the great things I like about myself.
I am AWESOME!

A big thank you to my dear colleague and pediatric therapist, Robyn Fatseas, whom I consulted with several times to make sure I was delivering the most accurate and effective advice to my young audience. Robyn has a clinic in Quincy, Massachusetts, where she specializes in complex child development, anxiety, and bullying. Visit robynsnestpsychology.com for more information.

The first book in the series:

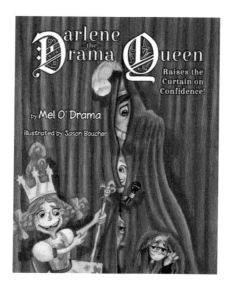

About the Author

Melanie was born in Dublin, Ireland, and moved to the USA in 1994. She grew up in a theatrical family and theatre became a second home to her at an early age. She received her BFA in Theatre Training at Emerson College in Boston, and went on to perform in many theatre roles. In 2006, she landed a role in a soap opera in Ireland playing the part of the devious Annemarie Murphy. She moved back to Boston in 2008 with her husband, and they now live in Quincy with their two sons, James and Patrick. In 2011, she founded the Mel O'Drama School of Acting in Milton, Massachusetts, and teaches several sessions, camps, and workshops in Milton, Quincy, and surrounding towns throughout the year. Empowering children and arming them with the tools they need to face troubling issues is something Melanie sees as vital and very rewarding. Working on confidence, awareness, and helping people to let go and HAVE FUN is at the core of Melanie's work. For more information on Melanie and her work, visit melodramakids.com.